THE FIELD MUSEUM

THE FIELD MUSEUM

Cheryl Bardoe

BECKON BOOKS

Table of Contents

INTRODUCTION
A Legacy of Life
7

PART ONE
A World-Class Museum
9

PART TWO
The Exhibitions
19

PART THREE
Beyond Museum Walls
69

AFTERWORD
The Work Continues
79

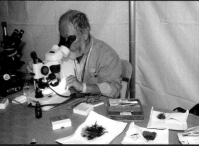

MUSES IN NORTH COLONNADE
The statues in the north colonnade—*Science*
(left) and *Dissemination of Knowledge*—were
inspired by and symbolize the Museum's mission.

A LEGACY OF LIFE

*"Make no little plans; they have no magic to stir men's blood and
probably will themselves not be realized. Make big plans; aim high in hope and work."*
—Architect Daniel Burnham, who designed
The Field Museum's landmark building

When the World's Fair came to Chicago in 1893, civic leaders recognized a unique opportunity to create a world-class museum. Thousands of artifacts and specimens were already on display in the fair's Anthropology Building. These collections, the men believed, could be powerful tools for teaching people about life on earth. So after the fair closed, they acquired the displays to launch a permanent new museum.

Today, The Field Museum is one of the world's largest museums of natural history, caring for the legacy of more than 24 million artifacts and specimens. What can visitors discover from standing in the presence of the world's largest, most complete *T. rex* skeleton? Or from examining a spear point made razor sharp by human hands 13,000 years ago? Or witnessing the earth's incredible diversity of plants and animals? An average of 1.4 million people come to the Museum each year to find out.

While visitors find inspiration in the Museum's 310,000 square feet of exhibition halls, more than 150 Museum scientists investigate the inner workings of nature and culture. Their work behind the scenes and around the world helps to preserve the earth's environment, strengthen cultural communities, and build scientific knowledge that may be used to address the urgent concerns of modern times.

CHICAGO'S MUSEUM CAMPUS
The Field Museum, shown at far left, is neighbor to Shedd Aquarium, Adler Planetarium, and Soldier Field.

STANLEY FIELD HALL
For nearly a century, this grand hall, left, has featured iconic attractions, including the *T. rex* Sue and the fighting African elephants.

PART ONE

A WORLD-CLASS MUSEUM

"Not to take advantage of the golden opportunity now offered . . . would simply be choosing to remain in the darkness of ignorance when one of the brightest lights for culture is within reach."

—Anthropologist Dr. Frederic Putnam, advocating for the creation of The Field Museum, 1890

The story of The Field Museum began when Chicago set its sights on hosting the World's Columbian Exposition, or World's Fair, of 1893. At the time, Chicago was the nation's second largest city. It was also a major steel center, the birthplace of the modern skyscraper, and home to 1,138 hotels and 38 railroads. Naysayers on the East Coast suggested that a World's Fair held in Chicago would amount to no more than an overgrown county fair. Chicago civic leaders banded together, however, and won their case before congress.

The Columbian Exposition opened on May 1, 1893, and turned out to be one of the largest and most successful world's fairs ever. The elegant buildings, fountains, and plazas of the fairgrounds were soon dubbed "the White City by Lake Michigan." Forty-six nations participated in the fair, which featured more than 200 buildings covering 630 acres. Displays ranged from mechanized milking machines, to priceless art, to an 11-ton block of cheese. And visitors could enjoy it all for 25 cents.

The fair attracted 27 million visitors, equal to half the U.S. population at that time. It only lasted six months, but it influenced industry, architecture, and urban planning for decades. One of its most enduring legacies came from the Anthropology Building— which some considered a fiasco at the time.

WINDOWS TO THE WORLD
Artifacts such as this headdress, far left, and house post, left, offered 1893 fairgoers the chance of a lifetime to encounter cultures from around the globe. The grizzly bear house post once towered near a Bella Coola longhouse in British Columbia. The feather headdress was made by the Jivaro tribe of Peru.

A MUSEUM IN THE MAKING

In 1891, fair directors put Harvard professor Dr. Frederic Putnam in charge of the anthropology displays. Putnam amassed the largest such display attempted to date, with artifacts gathered from every continent. His vision, however, didn't match the fair's allotted space and schedule. At Putnam's request, fair directors squeezed a new building—devoted to anthropology—onto the fairgrounds. This afterthought was off the beaten path and not completed until July, more than two months after the fair opened.

Putnam was motivated by a long-term scheme. As early as 1890, he had been appealing to civic leaders to fund a permanent museum at the fair's conclusion. In a letter to the *Chicago Tribune*, Putnam wrote: "To this great city is now offered an exceptional opportunity of establishing a grand museum of natural history." Hoping to create a ready-made museum in the Anthropology Building, he made room for fossils and geological displays alongside the cultural exhibits.

The idea of a permanent museum also appealed to Chicago businessman Edward E. Ayer, who heard Putnam speak at an 1891 meeting of

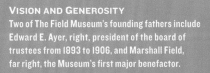

the Chicago Commercial Club and later became the Museum's first president. Growing up in rural Wisconsin and Illinois, Ayer attended school just three months each year before dropping out at age 11. He went on to work at his father's farm and dry goods store, toil in a Utah quartz mine, and serve in the California Civil War cavalry. Ayer ultimately made his fortune supplying timber for railroad ties. As his wealth grew, he traveled, read, collected artifacts, and sought ways to share what he had seen of the world.

Ayer didn't have deep enough pockets to put a museum on the map, but he knew someone who did: department store magnate Marshall Field. Field, however, was not an easy sell. He had heard about the museum for months, but was reluctant to get involved. "I don't want to know anything about a museum," Field had grumbled early on.

Undaunted, Ayer approached Field shortly before the fair closed. "If I can't talk you out of a million dollars in 15 minutes," he said, "I'm no good, nor you either."

Intrigued by the challenge, Field replied, "Fire ahead."

Ayer pointed out that a great businessman from the previous generation was almost completely forgotten. Field would face the same fate unless he created a legacy that fulfilled more than the need to purchase the perfect hat. By funding a museum, Ayer explained, Field could "have the privilege of being the educational host of untold millions of people."

Forty-five minutes later, Field was still listening and had agreed to tour the fair exhibits that would be desirable for a museum. Two days later, he wrote a check for one million dollars.

Whale Skeleton

When this skeleton was displayed at the World's Fair, it represented one of the most hunted species of whales. Yet few Americans living away from the East Coast would have ever seen one. Early whalers dubbed this species the "Right Whale" (as in, the correct whale to hunt) because it swam close to shore, floated after being killed, and provided lots of blubber. Protected by international laws since the 1930s, Right Whales remain the rarest of large whales. This impressive skeleton currently hangs in the Museum's animal halls, reminding visitors of the majesty of life swimming in the oceans.

SHIPPED BY CAMEL!
Museum scientists traveled
through Abyssinia (Ethiopia),
Africa, from 1926 to 1927. Frequent
expeditions quickly increased the
Museum's scientific collections
during its early decades.

FORGING A NEW IDENTITY

The Field Columbian Museum launched in 1894 in what had been the fair's Palace of Fine Arts. The original institution commemorated the World's Fair and featured exhibits on transportation and industrial arts as well as natural history. The Museum immediately dispatched scientists across the globe to collect dinosaur bones, excavate ancient ruins, and catalogue as much of nature as they could. People now talked about The Field Museum as they had once talked about the World's Fair. Writing from the Museum's first expedition to Africa, Zoology curator Daniel Elliot promised, "We will make The Field Columbian Museum lick all creation as a scientific museum and a Mecca for all naturalists to visit."

With such enthusiasm, the botany, anthropology, zoology, and geology collections couldn't help but crowd out materials in other fields, which were gradually redistributed to other organizations. In 1905, the institution was renamed The Field Museum of Natural History, which today has been shortened to simply The Field Museum.

It wasn't long before the Museum needed a new home to accompany its new name. The graceful buildings of the World's Fair had been erected of plaster, never intended to last, and most of the buildings had been destroyed by fire in 1894. The Palace of Fine Arts had hung on, but just barely. By 1897, the roof leaked constantly, and by 1905, the Museum had erected fences around the exterior to protect passersby from falling mortar. By 1913, the storage rooms were so full that the walkways were only two feet wide.

Architecture aficionados saw a silver lining, though. Here was a chance to design an extraordinary structure with exhibitions, collections, and research all in one building—and with space to grow. Celebrated architect Daniel Burnham designed the Museum's new building. Envisioning it as a temple to learning, he applied the Beaux Arts style he had used at the World's Fair.

Construction began in 1915 on a parcel of man-made lakefront that the Illinois Central Railroad had

traded to a predecessor of the Chicago Park District for other land. The land was a sea of mud without so much as a weed. For the first year of construction, rail cars needed to haul in landfill to raise the surface level 30 feet before the Museum's basement floor could begin. Builders then started wood pilings below lake level to stabilize the foundation and extended them as far as 95 feet down to solid rock. These were topped with 30-foot concrete piers that reached up to support the Museum floor. After five years and $7 million, the building was complete (although still surrounded by mud). Moving into the new building took six months, with 354 loads of specimens arriving by truck and 321 boxcar loads by rail.

Eight thousand people attended the Museum's reopening on May 2, 1921. Outside, the building's white marble gleamed in the sun and elegant pediments crowned its main entrances. Inside, flowing arcades and ionic columns framed the Stanley Field Hall, while symmetry organized the long galleries that extended to each side. Sculptural details throughout the building hearkened back to ancient

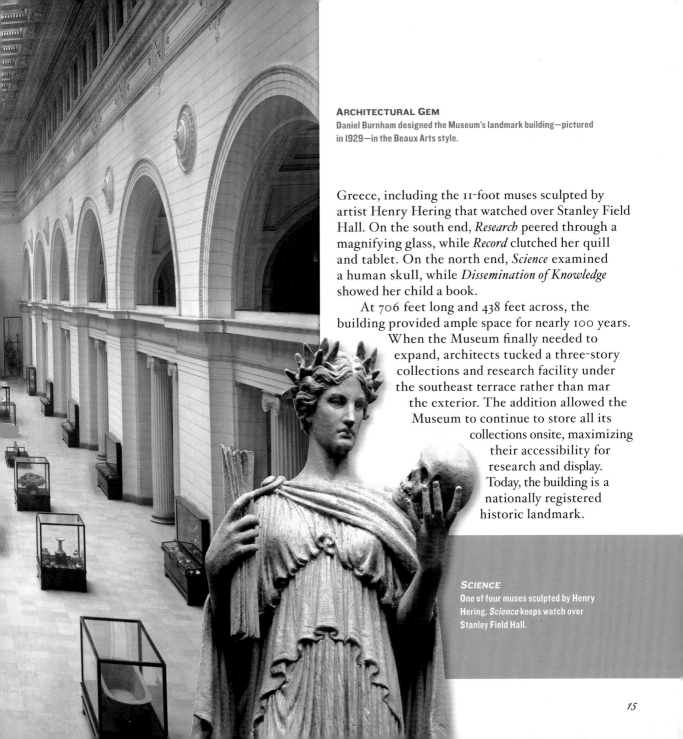

Greece, including the 11-foot muses sculpted by
artist Henry Hering that watched over Stanley Field
Hall. On the south end, *Research* peered through a
magnifying glass, while *Record* clutched her quill
and tablet. On the north end, *Science* examined
a human skull, while *Dissemination of Knowledge*
showed her child a book.

At 706 feet long and 438 feet across, the
building provided ample space for nearly 100 years.
When the Museum finally needed to
expand, architects tucked a three-story
collections and research facility under
the southeast terrace rather than mar
the exterior. The addition allowed the
Museum to continue to store all its
collections onsite, maximizing
their accessibility for
research and display.
Today, the building is a
nationally registered
historic landmark.

CASTING CULTURES

In 1930, Malvina Hoffman set off with 122 letters of introduction printed on official Museum letterhead. From Morocco to Mongolia to Malaysia, she traveled the world, seeking subjects for bronze portraits. A student of French sculptor Auguste Rodin, Hoffman also visited foundries to learn the art of metalworking. She used carpentry and plumbing tools and did her own heavy lifting to show that a woman could master bronze casting as well as a man. Her 104 bronze sculptures capture individual personalities from many cultures. Forty-four of them are still on display.

A 21st-Century Museum

As The Field Museum's scientific collections, research, and educational programs have grown, so has its international reputation. Inside the Museum, visitors can see the largest nongovernment collection of meteorites in the world; one of the world's largest and most comprehensive bird collections; one of the world's finest collections of Pacific Island artifacts; one of the world's largest collections of artifacts from Plains American Indians; the third largest mammal collection in the nation; the fourth finest collection of fossil fishes in the world; the fifth finest collection of flowering plants in the nation; and much more.

Answers to some of the 21st century's most pressing problems lie in this carefully catalogued library of the earth's history, nature's diversity, and human culture. The more scientists and citizens understand about the world's natural and cultural diversity, the better they can maintain healthy ecosystems, capitalize on the similarities and differences between cultures, and foster a high quality of life for everyone.

Today, The Field Museum is joined on Chicago's Museum Campus by two other acclaimed institutions: Shedd Aquarium and Adler Planetarium, which both opened in 1930. What was long ago a sea of mud is now a celebrated hub of questioning and acquiring knowledge—like the once gleaming World's Fair, but without the 11-ton block of cheese, and this time built to last.

An Incredible Collection

Visitors often marvel at the number of objects displayed at The Field Museum, yet the exhibitions only feature about one-tenth of one percent of its collections. The Museum is home to more than 24 million objects, each tagged with the date, locality, and circumstances of its collection. Highlights include 157,000 samples of fungi (pressed and affixed to herbarium sheets); 20,942 clutches of bird eggs (each egg drained, no matter how small); more than 1 million specimens (representing over 7,000 species) of rove beetles; mammals from 190 countries (representing every mammal family except the bumblebee bats from Western Thailand, which are possibly the world's smallest mammals); 30,000 fish fossils; 7,500 paper rubbings made from revered stone carvings in China; and 225,000 artifacts from indigenous cultures of North America.

To continue housing this vast collection, the Museum built an 186,000-square-foot, state-of-the-art collections and research center under the southeast terrace in 2006. Because temperature fluctuations, humidity, and dust are known enemies of scientific collections, this facility is equipped to filter pollutants from the air and maintain a climate of 68 degrees and 50 percent humidity. Individual shelves can hold 25-foot canoes or 12,500 pounds of fossilized dinosaur bones. Meanwhile, entire cabinets can be rolled closely together with the turn of a wheel to maximize space.

Why does the Museum collect so much? Because it is only after the analysis of many, many examples that scientific collections will divulge their secrets. These millions of objects provide mountains of data that are equal to conducting numerous experimental trials. They are vital evidence of dynamic biological and social change.

Scientists used Museum collections, for example, to identify species for a 2008 global status report on mammals. The five-year project—led by the International Union for Conservation of Nature and involving seven Museum scientists—increased the number of known mammal species by 20 percent. It also revealed that one in four mammal species is threatened with extinction. In addition, The Field Museum and the University of Chicago are using specimens to investigate the species-switching pathogens that can result in diseases such as bird flu, Ebola, malaria, and AIDS. And Museum anthropologists are studying artifacts from a resilient empire in ancient Peru in hopes of learning community strategies for surviving drought.

CATS WITHOUT CONTEXT
An 1899 display at The Field Columbian Museum presents lions and cougars in isolation, independent of any background.

PART TWO

THE EXHIBITIONS

"The Field Museum will move as the world moves, forever keeping abreast of the times and the changes which they bring."
—Stanley Field, president
of The Field Museum (1908–1962)

Witnessing the scale, diversity, and three-dimensional reality of the Museum's treasures is every bit as awe inspiring today as it was a century ago. The surrounding elements, however, are dramatically different. When The Field Museum opened in 1894, its geology hall consisted solely of mahogany cases spaced in precise rows 12 feet apart and packed with specimens. Brief, handwritten ID tags left visitors to interpret for themselves the meaning of what they were seeing. In contrast, today's *Evolving Planet* exhibition combines fossils, multimedia landscapes, videos, graphics, lighting effects, models, and 150 hands-on interactives that communicate the scientific story of 4 billion years of life on earth.

Almost one-third of the Museum's permanent exhibition space has been renovated since the 21st century began, and more than half in the last 25 years. Meanwhile, the Museum's classic galleries retain scientific and educational value, and other galleries change constantly with temporary exhibitions. The 1977 King Tut exhibition attracted 1.4 million visitors in four months and sparked a nationwide media sensation. In more recent years, the Museum has exhibited the Dead Sea Scrolls from Israel, original frescoes from Pompeii, and a 40,000-year-old baby mammoth that was so well preserved it appeared to be sleepwalking.

MAMMOTHS AND MASTODONS
The Museum's contemporary exhibitions use atmospheric settings, bold graphics, and interactive media to engage visitors in the stories behind artifacts and specimens.

FROM IDEAS TO EXHIBITIONS

Crafting an environment that will entertain, educate, and inspire millions of visitors from around the world for potentially more than a decade is the work of far more than one person. Large-scale permanent halls like *The Ancient Americas* and *Evolving Planet* begin as kernels of ideas, perhaps born of new discoveries, or from topics of high public interest. Curators and exhibition developers then give form to these ideas, articulating scientific stories that will provide visitors with a deeper understanding of the natural and cultural world.

To bring these ideas to life, scientists and developers venture into Museum treasure vaults to choose artifacts, fossils, and specimens. Conservators, designers, mount makers, and master builders join the effort, and each exhibition features some combination of images, text, interactives, films, replicated models, and recreated environments. For instance, the 27,000-square-foot *Evolving Planet* exhibition was created by dozens of scientists and more than 100 exhibitions staff over the course of five years. A similarly sized team worked for about the same amount of time on *The Ancient Americas*. Meanwhile, countless Museum staff and volunteers maintain the temperature and humidity of the galleries, clean display cases, take tickets, lead school field trip workshops, and perform a myriad of other duties that make each exhibition accessible to visitors every day.

SUE

The *Tyrannosaurus rex (T. rex)* known as Sue is an icon not only of The Field Museum, but also of the city of Chicago. More than 16 million visitors have gazed upon Sue since her skeleton was unveiled in 2000. At 40.5 feet long, Sue is an intriguing combination of massive thighbones and delicate arms—as well as powerful jaws and 12-inch, dagger-like teeth that reveal what a powerful predator *T. rex* must have been. Only six of the 40 *T. rex* skeletons ever found are more than 40 percent complete. None compare to Sue, the largest, who is 90 percent complete and so well preserved that her bones retain the imprints from clinging tendons. (Fossilization, however, has transformed her milk-white bones to a deep brown over the course of 67 million years.)

Sue is named for fossil hunter Sue Hendrickson, who spotted the specimen's vertebrae jutting from a South Dakota cliff in 1990. The skeleton was sold at auction in 1997, with most of the bones still in plaster field jackets. To prevent this fossil from being

SUE'S NAMESAKE
Bad luck turned to good fortune when Sue Hendrickson, right, discovered a *T. rex* (later also named Sue) while waiting for a flat tire to be fixed.

SUE UNCRATED
The bones of the *T. rex* Sue, including the right thigh bone, far right, were encased in protective plaster for transport to the Museum.

FLESH AND BONES
Sue's mounted skeleton guards Stanley Field Hall while paleoartist John Gurche's mural depicts this impressive dinosaur in the flesh.

A HEAVY HEAD
Too massive to be mounted, Sue's head is installed in an exhibit case on the Museum's second floor. A replica of her head sits atop the skeleton downstairs.

purchased by a private owner—and science and the public losing an extraordinary window into the prehistoric past—the Museum assembled a coalition of funders that enabled it to withstand other bidders, securing the skeleton for $8.36 million.

Since then, Sue has become the Rosetta Stone of dinosaurs. A CT scan of her skull was created from 748 specialized X-ray images, each representing a two-millimeter slice of skull. It revealed that *T. rex* dinosaurs primarily smelled their way through life with olfactory lobes nearly as big as their brains. Sue's ribs and smaller bones also helped scientists uncover the dramatic growth rate that occurred in *T. rex* dinosaurs between the ages of 11 and 14. Despite hatching from eggs that were likely smaller than footballs, these animals grew to weigh more than 11,000 pounds by bulking up during their teen years at an average of 4.6 pounds a day, for a cumulative 1,650 pounds per year. In addition, Museum curator Dr. Peter Makovicky is studying a virtual model of Sue that was made with the help of a police forensics team that surveyed her with the same laser scanners used to create computer models of crime scenes. Scientists can't predict all the discoveries Sue might lead them to in the future, but perhaps someday they will even determine the skeleton's gender—and at last resolve whether this famous dinosaur is actually a girl or a boy.

MAPPING THE BONES
Museum staff plan the assembly of the *T. rex* Sue, right.

MOUNT IN PROGRESS
Eight people labored for a combined total of 20,000 hours to design, engineer, and build the mount that supports Sue's bones, far right.

McDonald's Fossil Preparation Laboratory

From worktables that support 2,000-pound rocks to an exhaust system that vacuums dust particles from the air, the *McDonald's Fossil Preparation Laboratory* is equipped with everything needed to free fossils from the sand and stone that grip them. Here, miniature jackhammers chip away hard matrix, while sand-blasters scour away softer material with a steady barrage of baking soda. The most powerful tool of all, however, is the staff's patience in following the lines of fossils as they emerge bit by bit, layer by layer, bone by bone. Scientists are as eager as visitors to view full specimens, but they know that hurrying might damage fragile fossils.

A dozen people spent 30,000 hours to remove three tons of matrix from the bones of Sue the *T. rex*—enough work to keep one person busy full time for 12 years!

Many of those hours were on view in this lab. In addition to dinosaur bones, visitors can watch lab workers prepare fish, plant, and invertebrate fossils here.

CAMBRIAN MARINE SCENE
Artist Karen Carr relied on fossil evidence to envision scenes from past eras for *Evolving Planet*.

EVOLVING PLANET

Evolving Planet opened in 2006 to tell the history of four billion years of life on earth. Spanning 27,000 square feet, it features 1,300 fossils, as well as scientific models, murals, 150 hands-on interactives, and videos. The exhibition begins with the explosion of life in the earth's early seas—amidst frequent volcanic eruptions and meteor showers—and follows life's eventual migration onto land. It then traces the five prehistoric mass extinctions that periodically wiped out 50 percent, 70 percent, and even 90 percent of living species, each time creating room for new life forms to blossom in a freshly altered environment. Throughout, fossils provide physical evidence of evolution, while interviews with scientists explain their findings about this process of nature.

Fossils are the starting point for a multimedia projection in *Evolving Planet* that surrounds visitors with animations of ancient creatures from the shallow Cambrian seas. The animals may look bizarre, but the fossils on display prove they once existed—and that they represent nearly all the major groups of animals still on earth. Other fossils inspired the exhibition's life-sized recreation of a 300-million-year-old swampy forest, complete with gargantuan insects. Some of the world's best fossils from this era (which fueled the world's coal beds) have been found near Mazon Creek, just 60 miles southwest of Chicago.

Dinosaurs are another popular part of the exhibition, with every major group on display. Representatives include the *Herrerasaurus* (one of the earliest known meat-eating dinosaurs), the armored *Stegosaurus*,

EXQUISITE FOSSILS
Museum excavations at Wyoming's Fossil Lake have revealed many finely preserved fossils from the Eocene Epoch, approximately 50 million years ago. These include *Priscacara serrata*, a spiny-finned teleost fish, right, and *Heliobatis radians*, a stingray, far right.

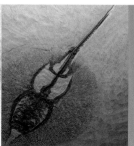

LUCY
Artist Elisabeth Daynes created this life-sized model of the famous early hominid identified as *Australopithicus afarensis*, later dubbed "Lucy."

and the duck-billed *Parasaurolophus*. Old discoveries are highlighted, such as the *Brachiosaurus* bones that were first identified in 1900, along with recent fossil evidence that relates dinosaurs to modern birds.

After the mass extinction that ended the dinosaurs' reign, mammals flourished. From this era, *Evolving Planet* features the world's oldest-known bat fossil and the skeletons of giant sloths and mighty mammoths. The Hominid gallery gives a concise overview of the human family tree that emerged about 8 million years ago. Here, casts of some of the world's most famous hominid fossils—along with lifelike reconstructions of their hands and faces—compare these species to modern humans. A highlight of this gallery is the standing, smiling reconstruction of the hominid fossil known as "Lucy," which lived in Africa 3.2 million years ago.

The exhibition concludes by describing the sixth mass extinction that is occurring today. Throughout the earth's history, the average rate of extinction has been one species every four years. Recent human activity,

DINOSAURS GALORE
From skeletons to models to murals, *Evolving Planet* features *Triceratops*, *Parasaurolophus*, *Herrerasaurus*, *Stegosaurus*, and more.

EXPLORING LIFE ON EARTH
A small sampling of biodiversity welcomes visitors to *Evolving Planet*, a 27,000-square-foot exhibition that traces the history of life over 4 billion years.

however, has brought about a massive loss of habitat, causing 30,000 species to go extinct each year. This information puts the rest of the Museum's mission in perspective, proving that the more society understands the processes of cultural and natural diversity, the better it can sustain a healthy habitat on this constantly evolving planet.

EVOLVING SCIENCE

The exhibits in *Evolving Planet* are based on research by scientists who study everything from dinosaurs to tiny invertebrates to ancient hominids. One section of the gallery, for instance, compares the skeletons of prehistoric theropods (meat-eating dinosaurs that ran on two feet) with that of a modern chicken. These common features are important to Museum curator Dr. Peter Makovicky.

In 2002, he co-authored a paper that described one of the first fossils to conclusively demonstrate the link between dinosaurs and their modern-day descendants—birds. The new species, named *Sinovenator changii*, was about the size of a large chicken and lived 130 million years ago in what is now China. Today, Dr. Makovicky's research is contributing to an international effort to chart a family tree for dinosaurs.

ERNST & YOUNG 3-D THEATER
Opened in 2009 and showcasing a variety of films each year, Chicago's only completely digital 3-D theater brings visitors face to face with a rotating selection of favorite exhibition subjects—including mummies and dinosaurs.

"Short-faced" Bear (*Arctodus simus*)
This huge mammal lived during the Pleistocene Epoch
(1.8 million to 10,000 years ago).

Charles Knight Murals

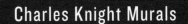

If the murals in *Evolving Planet* seem familiar, that's because they set the standard for paleoart over much of the last century. In 1926, the Museum commissioned preeminent muralist Charles R. Knight to create 28 scenes of life on earth from its earliest origins. Legally blind since the age of six, Knight painted his masterpieces with his nose almost touching the canvas, combining an artist's imagination with a scientist's knowledge of anatomy and fossils. The project took four years to complete, and the images have since been reproduced in countless textbooks. Although these murals no longer reflect the latest scientific discoveries, they continue to evoke the ambiance of eras gone by.

Evolving Planet also examines animals that lived alongside the dinosaurs, including tiny fossils called bryozoans, which may reveal important information about the history of life on earth. Bryozoans are aquatic creatures that live in colonies from two to two million individuals. Museum paleontologist Dr. Scott Lidgard studies these animals, which have been around for 500 million years and still exist in huge numbers today. Because bryozoans are small and live in locales that are commonly covered in sediments, they are well represented in the fossil record. With so much information about the diversity and abundance of these creatures over millions of years, scientists like Dr. Lidgard can investigate major questions about competitiveness between species, how the presence of predators might influence adaptation, the invasion of new environments, and changes in the climate or ocean chemistry.

Another museum curator, Dr. Robert Martin, contributed to *Evolving Planet's* exhibits on the origins of modern humans. Dr. Martin is a biological anthropologist who researches the history of primates. In his quest to achieve a reliable reconstruction of primate evolutionary history, Dr. Martin studies an array of primate characteristics, including anatomy, physiology, chromosomes, and DNA. Although the earliest known primate fossils are 55 million years old, statistical analysis allowing for gaps in the fossil record indicates that primates actually diverged from other mammals about 85 million years ago. When this result is applied to human evolution, it appears that this lineage probably branched off around 8 million years ago, earlier than previously thought.

MID-DEVONIAN LIFE
Museum dioramas recreate the bryozoans, trilobites, snails, and corals of the inland seas that once covered the Great Lakes and Ohio River regions.

BRACHIOSAURUS BENCHMARK
Paleontologist Elmer Riggs discovered the first known *Brachiosaurus*. The bones became the holotype, or physical example, by which other *Brachiosaurus* fossils are compared for identification.

THEN AND NOW: COLOSSAL FOSSIL DISCOVERIES

Although *Evolving Planet* didn't open until the 21st century, the buzz about fossils was as big when the Museum was first established as it is today. When Museum paleontologist Elmer Riggs uncovered the largest humerus (upper limb bone) of any dinosaur known in 1900, he wrote to colleagues to keep the discovery quiet so that competing fossil-hunters wouldn't encroach on his mother lode. Riggs returned to the Museum with six tons of fossils, including the type specimen of *Brachiosaurus*, which is still one of the largest known dinosaurs.

In contrast, modern-day paleontologist Dr. Lance Grande posts updates and video reports about his field-work for thousands of fans to read at www.fieldmuseum.org/expeditions. Dr. Grande has been excavating the Green River formation in Wyoming for more than 25 years. This 18-inch layer of limestone—one of the richest fossil deposits in the world—preserves a snapshot of an entire lake ecosystem that thrived 50 million years ago. Although Dr. Grande and his team

BACK AT THE LAB
Elmer Riggs and his assistant Harold W. Menke, far left, prepare fossils from a dig in Grand Junction, Colorado, in 1899.

OUT IN THE FIELD
Dr. Lance Grande, left, wields a power saw while excavating fossils in southwestern Wyoming in 2003.

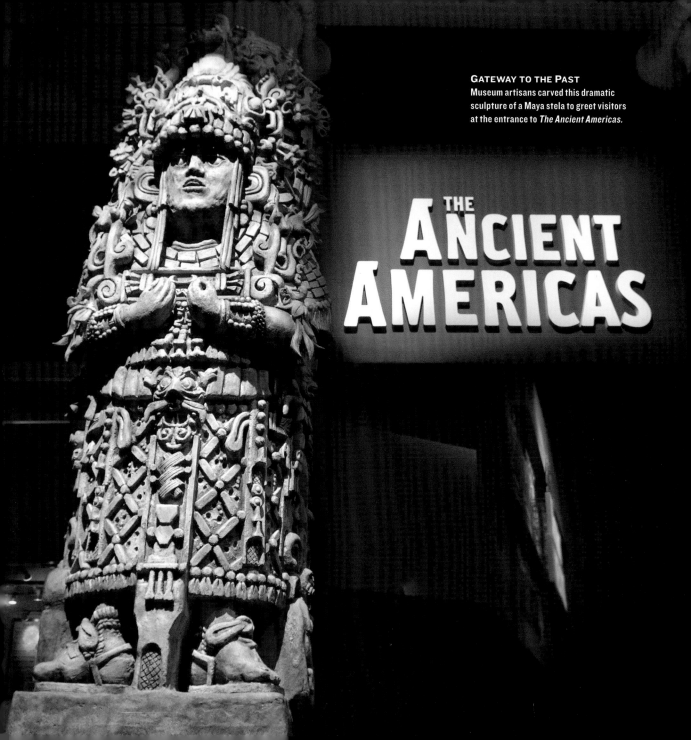

THE ANCIENT AMERICAS

do use bulldozers and power saws, most of
their hard labor of splitting the limestone into
quarter-inch layers is done with old-fashioned
shovels, picks, and sledgehammers. Antici-
pation keeps the team motivated, because
each new slab may reveal a 13-foot crocodile,
a bird with feathers, a giant palm frond, or a
stingray. A selection of these incredible fossils
is featured in *Evolving Planet*.

THE ANCIENT AMERICAS

People living today may have more in common
with Ice Age hunters, Hopi cliff dwellers, or
Incan messengers than they realize. *The Ancient
Americas*, which opened in 2007, highlights how
all cultures continually evolve through human creativity and problem solving. This 19,000-square-
foot exhibition combines the latest archaeological research with 2,200 artifacts, videos,
recreated environments, and hands-on interactives to
examine 20 cultures that have populated the Western
Hemisphere. Throughout the exhibition, graphics and
videos show how descendants of indigenous American
cultures retain and celebrate their heritage today.

The exhibition welcomes visitors with a dramatic
media landscape of Ice Age hunters and mammoths

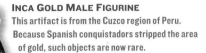

INCA GOLD MALE FIGURINE
This artifact is from the Cuzco region of Peru.
Because Spanish conquistadors stripped the area
of gold, such objects are now rare.

roaming the Chicago area 13,000 years ago.
Rather than being arranged chronologically,
however, *The Ancient Americas* focuses on how
different cultures organize their everyday
activities. Curators chose this approach to
illustrate that hunters and gatherers are no
more primitive than empire builders. From the
chiseled spear points of Ice Age Clovis people to
the gold figurines that flaunted rank in
Colombian society, this array of artifacts testi-
fies to the efforts and inventiveness of human
beings in meeting the challenges of life.

The theme of commonality is highlighted
throughout the gallery. Black and white pottery
created by Southwestern Pueblo people nearly 1,000
years ago reveals the essential human urge to create.
Portrait vessels from ancient Peru illustrate how each
person living in the Moche culture 1,500 years ago—
from elite warriors to humble water carriers—was as
unique as each individual living today. The diorama of
an Aztec marketplace also hints that many aspects of

CARVING OF LADY XOK
This cast is of a Maya altar panel found
in Yaxchilan, Mexico. The original is over
1,000 years old.

TO MARKET, TO MARKET
This handcrafted diorama depicts the thriving shopping district of Tlatelolco, Mexico, in 1515.

life have not changed. With 251 miniature people selling 50 different commodities, this diorama was based on eyewitness accounts from conquistadors in 1519. It brings the ancient bazaar to life, right down to the children playing pranks and customers tussling over a bolt of fine cloth.

THEN AND NOW: GREAT CIVILIZATIONS UNCOVERED

The artifacts and scholarship utilized in *The Ancient Americas* reflect more than 100 years of research and collection. Some artifacts in this exhibition, for example, were found during excavations commissioned for the 1893 World's Fair. At that time, the presence of giant, human-made earth mounds in Ohio perplexed European explorers and pioneers. Unwilling to believe that Native Americans could have built such elaborate structures, Europeans attributed the earthworks to Celts, Asians, or Egyptians. Yet the obsidian blades, copper ear spools, mica carvings, pearl beads, and many other artifacts excavated from the mounds revealed these structures to be built by another distinct

culture—the Hopewell people. The World's Fair introduced many people to this artistic, technologically sophisticated civilization, which had extensive trade routes and flourished for centuries.

Such excavation work is ongoing. Today, Dr. Gary Feinman and Dr. Linda Nicholas conduct fieldwork in Oaxaca, Mexico, which was also an area of interest for the Museum's first anthropology curator, William Henry Holmes. Over the years, many Museum anthropologists have studied cultures throughout North, South, and Central America to understand how and why cultures change, as well as how contemporary people thrive in the modern world.

In 2000, curator Dr. Jonathan Haas and a team of North American and Peruvian colleagues decided

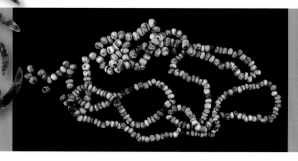

MOUNDBUILDERS
Nearly 2,000 years ago, the Hopewell culture thrived in what is now the Midwest. It left behind artifacts such as this mica eagle foot effigy, right, and necklaces of freshwater pearls, far right.

TEOTIHUACAN MASK
This mask was carved from stone around 500 C.E. With
an estimated population of 125,000 people, the city of
Teotihuacan was then one of the largest cities in the world.

economic and religious systems. They have concluded
that despite the lack of pottery, Caral was built by a
complex civilization at the same time Egyptians built
their earliest pyramids more than 5,000 years ago—
making it the earliest known city in the Americas.

Another anthropology curator, Dr. Ryan Williams,
has uncovered a 1,000-year-old brewery in the highlands of Peru. Using a ground-penetrating radar and a
magnometer, which measures anomalies in the earth's
magnetic field, Dr. Williams found a cache of mugs
and brewing jars. These artifacts revealed a brewery
from the Wari culture, which fermented maize into
drink for important ceremonies. After Dr. Williams
returned to the lab, he used a mass spectrometer to
analyze the chemical composition of the artifacts and
identify trade patterns for the brewery. The Wari
culture represented South America's biggest empire
before the Inca and is featured in *The Ancient Americas*.
Its success as a culture—despite facing a 30-year
drought—may offer strategies for cultures facing
limited water supplies today.

to take a closer look at what lay beneath the sand drifts
of Caral. This ancient site near the coast of Peru was
found in 1905, but was largely ignored. Early discoverers
couldn't reconcile the site's advanced architecture and
irrigation with its lack of ceramics, traditionally
considered a sign of complex civilization. But Dr. Haas
and his colleagues found six pyramids there, the
largest being 60 feet tall and 450 feet by 500 feet at the
base. Since then, scientists have identified
a network of 19 other urban and ceremonial centers with the same terraced
pyramids, ceremonial plazas, and

MOCHE PORTRAIT VESSELS
The ancient Moche people of northern Peru frequently depicted
elite individuals through sculpture like this, far left, often creating
records of their childhood, adulthood, and even death.

WARI FIGURINE
This stone figurine, left, depicts an elaborately dressed leader—
distinguished by his headdress and tunic—of the Wari people
of south Peru, who lived from 500 to 1000 C.E.

Securing the Artifacts

If visitors never notice what secures the filigree of a Hopewell bronze ornament, or the heft of 250-pound Aztec stone, that's because they aren't supposed to. Nonetheless, mounts are what make it possible to display such treasures at all.

Most people don't notice minute vibrations occurring in the world because they are constantly in motion, too. Museum objects, however, feel the footsteps of visitors strolling through the exhibits, as well as the thud of steel beams being driven into bedrock for skyscrapers nearby. Over time, these vibrations can cause an object to slip off its shelf—or break.

The Americas galleries display more than 2,000 precious artifacts, each with a custom-made mount. Artisans skilled in sculpting, metal-working, and jewelry-making begin by cradling each object in their hands (with three or four people lifting heavy objects). Mount makers discern how objects balance, where they are most vulnerable, and what features would be most interesting to viewers. Then they spend anywhere from one hour to one month crafting unobtrusive bits of furniture to fix an item in its case without causing irreversible damage. When their work is done, it fades into the background, while putting the object's best face forward.

NORTHWEST AND ARCTIC CULTURES

NORTHWEST AND ARCTIC CULTURES
Demonstrating the ongoing vibrancy of Native American cultures, contemporary artists created the Cape Fox totem pole and arctic inuksuk for *The Alsdorf Hall of Northwest Coast and Arctic Peoples* in 2007.

Such excavations require careful research and planning. When Museum archaeologists begin their fieldwork, dig sites may look no different than other parts of the landscape—but scientific research suggests that more lies beneath the surface rocks and scrub brush. Archaeologists map out dig sites in two-meter squares, which are labeled and divided into quadrants. If the culture being studied is old enough to be buried deep, then scientists may use shovels and larger tools to remove topsoil. As they descend in time through the soil strata, they switch to hand trowels, brushes, and fine dental picks, removing the earth a centimeter at a time in search of new knowledge and discoveries that may someday be in a museum display.

OTHER NATIVE AMERICAN HALLS

While *The Ancient Americas* features 13,000 years of history in the Americas leading up to the arrival of Europeans, other galleries focus on native North American cultures in the 19th century. *The Alsdorf Hall of Northwest Coast and Arctic Peoples* exhibits artifacts collected around the turn of

KWAKIUTL TRANSFORMATION MASK
This mask, right, was made prior to 1893. It represents a sun/human composite and is constructed of carved and painted red cedar.

INUIT HUMAN FACE MASK
Masks like this one, far right, were inspired by intense visions from an angekok, or shaman.

the 20th century, when these groups struggled to maintain their distinctive lifestyles while facing increased contact with Western cultures. Masks reveal the striking differences between various Native American cultures, from the austere, bold aesthetic of Eskimos living on the harsh arctic tundra, to the more elaborate and colorful masks of the Northwest peoples who came from lush coastal forests farther south. Exploring these cultures side by side offers an intriguing look at how material culture is shaped by history, environment, and individual creativity—reminding visitors that diversity comes from different responses to the common concerns of human existence.

Near *The Alsdorf Hall of Northwest Coast and Arctic Peoples* is a full-size replica of a Pawnee earth lodge, framed by cottonwood tree trunks and willow lath. Such Pawnee lodges were built on the Great Plains

in the 1800s. Members of the Pawnee tribe advised on the building of this lodge and sang songs to bless this place of cultural exchange. The lodge is fully furnished with a fire pit, buffalo-robed sleeping platforms, and replicas of traditional Pawnee tools that visitors can touch. The 38-foot-diameter structure seats 45 people and is home to one of The Field Museum's most requested school programs.

The nearby North American Indians gallery also showcases a variety of clothing, ceramics, basketry, weaponry, beadwork, and children's toys created mostly in the 1800s by peoples from the Great Lakes, prairies, plains, and southwest regions of North America.

ABBOTT HALL OF CONSERVATION
RESTORING EARTH

Stepping into *Restoring Earth*, which opened in 2011, is like joining Museum scientists on a trek through a rainforest to inventory plants, birds, fishes, reptiles, amphibians, and mammals. Here, immersive media environments, interviews with scientists, and film footage of wilderness areas reveal the ways in which Museum scientists are working to conserve the world's biodiversity—important efforts that have led to new national parks and nature sanctuaries in biodiversity hotspots around the world.

Of course, conservation depends on the ability to use scientific data to benefit fragile ecosystems, as well as the people who live nearby. The Museum's Environment, Culture, and Conservation division, led by biologist Dr. Debra Moskovits, has pioneered a cross-disciplinary approach to meet this challenge. The Museum sends teams of two dozen or more scientists into a pristine wilderness area to conduct a "rapid biological inventory," recording as many plant and animal species as they can find to capture a snapshot of a region's biodiversity in just a few intense weeks of fieldwork. While biologists conduct their surveys, anthropologists meet with area residents. Local ecological knowledge, community resources, and the biological census are then synthesized into strategies to conserve a region's natural resources. Since the program's launch in 1999, the Museum has conducted 23 rapid biological inventories covering 32 million acres of forests, swamps, and mountains in South America, Cuba, and China.

To illustrate what scientists see when identifying distinct life forms, *Restoring Earth* includes both specimens and hands-on interactives. For example, a display of 99 mollusk shells from the Florida Keys includes extremes of size, shape, and color to complement a neighboring activity station. Visitors at the station can use magnification to sift through what appears to be sand and broken shells, and discover dozens more tiny, complete shells—shells that look similar but represent many individual mollusk species. This interactive parallels the work of curator Dr. Rüdiger Bieler and his colleagues, who discovered that there were more than three times the known species living in and near the Florida Keys National Marine Sanctuary than scientists had originally thought when the refuge was created in the 1990s. Such work provides a more comprehensive baseline for evaluating conservation efforts.

Daniel F. and Ada L. Rice DNA Discovery Center

⊰⋯⋯⊱

DNA is the thread that connects all forms of life, from microscopic bacteria to mushrooms to humans. The more researchers analyze genetic material, the closer they get to mapping out a "family tree" that documents the relationships among all species on earth.

The *DNA Discovery Center* offers a viewing window onto scientists at work in the Museum's *Pritzker Laboratory for Molecular Systematics and Evolution*. When the lab opened in 1974, it was one of the first such facilities at any natural history museum. The opening of the *DNA Discovery Center* in 2008 offered visitors one of the only public viewing windows onto this cutting edge work. Here, visitors can ask questions of the scientists and see them use state-of-the-art technology to extract, sequence, and analyze DNA. Surrounding videos and hands-on interactives answer basic and complex questions about DNA analysis and explore how genetic studies are changing scientists' understanding of biodiversity in the world.

DNA analysis is helping scientists investigate many important questions of animal lineage. For instance, despite their long necks and even longer legs, flamingos never seemed to fit in with birds of similar proportions. DNA analysis confirmed that flamingos are actually close cousins of grebes, which had never seemed to fit neatly among other species of waterfowl. In addition, DNA verified that despite looking and behaving similarly, falcons and hawks evolved through separate lineages. Based on these evolutionary findings, Museum ornithologist Dr. Shannon Hackett is leading an international effort to chart a new bird family tree. DNA analysis has enabled Dr. Hackett to look beyond the birds' appearances to find patterns that may illuminate the process of evolution and adaptation of many species.

Meanwhile, Museum ichthyologist Dr. Leo Smith is working on similar genetics projects to clarify evolutionary relationships among the more than 25,000 known species of fishes. He is particularly interested in venomous fishes, which are implicated in some 50,000 injuries each year. In addition to investigating the anatomy of preserved Museum specimens, Dr. Smith is analyzing more than one million base pairs of DNA sequence data. His studies have revealed that more than 2,000 species of fishes are venomous, far more than the previous estimate of 200. Such identifications and categorizations of fish venoms will go a long way in helping doctors respond effectively to venomous stings or perhaps even discover the next cancer treatment.

In addition, the gallery explores conservation work in urban areas like Chicago. The Museum partners with other organizations—supported by throngs of volunteers—to restore prairies, protect migrating birds, and battle invasive species throughout the Chicago region. *Restoring Earth* also tells the stories of various individuals to reveal how even small actions can create a big impact, illustrating the ways in which people find inspiration and connection through nature.

Throughout the hall, the Museum's commitment to green materials and building processes is evident. Paint was avoided wherever possible to minimize dispersal of volatile organic compounds into the atmosphere, and the carpet was chosen for its high content of pre- and post-consumer recycled materials. Many surfaces incorporate reclaimed wood from the Emerald Ash Borer Beetle infestation or fiberboard made of sorghum straw, an agricultural byproduct. Taken as a whole, *Restoring Earth* showcases the relationship between humans and the

FROM MACRO TO MICRO
Museum scientists seek to understand and preserve ecosystems that are as large as a forest (such as Peru's Cordillera Azul National Park, right) and organisms that are smaller than a dwarf cloud rat (from the Philippine islands, far right).

environment in a new way—recognizing that humans are just one more species in an ecosystem that needs a rich diversity of life forms to thrive.

GRAINGER HALL OF GEMS AND ELIZABETH HUBERT MALOTT HALL OF JADES

Fewer than 40 of the earth's 4,200 known minerals have the beauty, durability, and scarcity to qualify as true gemstones. The *Grainger Hall of Gems* highlights these wonders of nature, with more than 300 objects on display. The hall was renovated in 2009 to feature raw crystals alongside exquisite jewelry—revealing these precious stones to be as spectacular in their natural state as when precisely cut and polished, or incorporated into dazzling jewelry.

The Museum's gem collection was born out of the 1893 World's Fair. There, businessman Charles Lewis Tiffany organized such an impressive display that upon seeing it, Princess Eulalia and Prince Antonio of Spain honored Tiffany & Co. as a supplier of jewelry to her highness. Museum organizers purchased the collection in 1894 for $100,000 (the equivalent of more than $2.5 million today), and the Museum's collection has grown ever since.

TANZANITE PENDANT
Tanzanite was first discovered in 1967 and is 1,000 times rarer than diamond. This pendant features a 28.84-carat gemstone.

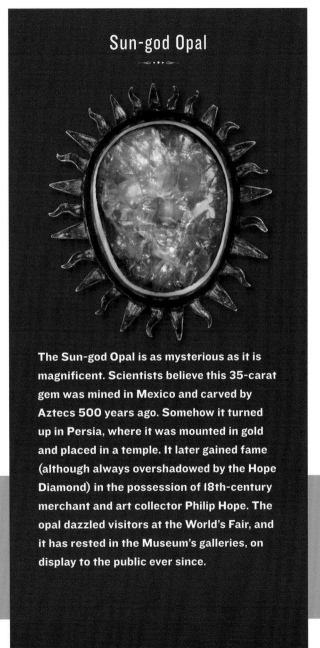

Sun-god Opal

The Sun-god Opal is as mysterious as it is magnificent. Scientists believe this 35-carat gem was mined in Mexico and carved by Aztecs 500 years ago. Somehow it turned up in Persia, where it was mounted in gold and placed in a temple. It later gained fame (although always overshadowed by the Hope Diamond) in the possession of 18th-century merchant and art collector Philip Hope. The opal dazzled visitors at the World's Fair, and it has rested in the Museum's galleries, on display to the public ever since.

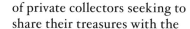

TIFFANY WINDOW
Louis Comfort Tiffany liked this piece so much that he kept it in his studio for many years. It was donated to the Museum in 1941.

The gallery's luminous stained glass window, with its mysterious mermaid and swirling seaweed, is the work of Tiffany's son, famed glass artist Louis Comfort Tiffany. The younger Tiffany's creations have often appeared alongside his father's gems, turning heads at the 1893 World's Fair, on the showfloor of Tiffany & Co., and now here at the Museum as well.

The *Elizabeth Hubert Malott Hall of Jades* focuses on a gemstone whose strength and splendor has inspired symbolism in cultures throughout history. Most of these 450 artifacts were collected in the early 1900s by Museum anthropologist Bertholt Laufer, then considered the Western world's foremost scholar on Chinese civilization. From jade disks found in 5,000-year-old graves to a 281-pound jar carved from a single jade boulder in the 1700s, this gallery explores the story of a cultural touchstone in China's past and present.

METEORITE COLLECTION

Just as stardust existed at the origin of the solar system, so meteorites were present at the birth of the Museum. In 1893, Ward's Natural Science Establishment displayed 170 meteorites at the World's Fair; Marshall Field purchased them all, and since then, the Museum's reputation for academic stewardship has continued to attract the attention of private collectors seeking to share their treasures with the

CHALMERS TOPAZ
Named for former Field Museum trustee William J. Chalmers, this cut topaz, right, is one of the largest such gems in the world.

JADEITE INCENSE BURNER
This burner, far right, is from China, the Qing period (1644 to 1911). Jadeite is one of two distinct minerals known as jade, and can appear in shades of bright green, lavender, and white.

HEATING ELEMENT
The inside of the Museum's mass spectrometer can get as hot as the surface of the sun.

public. Through donations, purchases, and field collecting, The Field Museum now has the largest nongovernment collection of meteorites in the world, with more than 2,000 distinct meteorites and 8,000-plus specimens.

The collection includes 19 of only 98 meteorites in the world that are believed to be from Mars (trapped gasses in the meteorites match those in Mars's atmosphere). Two of these are on display: the Lafayette meteorite, which was likely formed 1.3 billion years ago and tossed into space 11 million years ago; and the Zagami meteorite, which was probably formed by lava 180 million years ago and ejected from Mars 2.5 million years ago. In each case, scientists believe asteroids crashed into Mars with enough force to blast rubble into space and on a direct trajectory toward the earth's gravitational field.

To examine its world-class meteorite collection, the Museum uses state-of-the-art equipment at the *Robert A.*

Pritzker Center for Meteoritics and Polar Studies. Curator Dr. Phillip Heck uses a scanning electron microscope, mass spectrometer, and other tools to study pre-solar diamonds, which have been around longer than the solar system and are thousands of times smaller than an amoeba. These tiny grains are extracted from meteorites, which represent the first solid materials to form in the solar system, and are in essence the building blocks of planets. By examining the chemical makeup of pre-solar grains, Dr. Heck hopes to learn more about the environment of the early solar system and the delivery of extraterrestrial matter to earth.

INSIDE ANCIENT EGYPT

Despite his elaborate preparations for the afterlife, Pharaoh's son Unis-ankh probably never imagined that millions of people would be contemplating his life nearly 5,000 years after his death. Yet today, visitors to *Inside Ancient Egypt* can see two original chambers

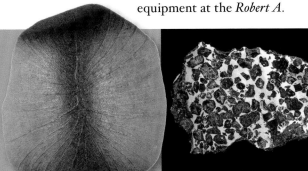

METEORITES FROM MARS?
Some meteorites in The Field Museum's collection like this one, far left, have an age and composition consistent with Martian volcanoes.

PALLASITES
Among the most lovely of meteorites, pallasites like this one, left, consist of olivine (peridot) crystals in a nickel-iron matrix.

RECREATED MASTABA OF UNIS-ANKH
Wealthier families from Egypt's 5th Dynasty buried loved ones in long, low mausoleums called mastabas. This full-size recreation contains two original rooms from Egypt.

from Unis-ankh's tomb, which help recreate a three-story mastaba. The Field Museum is one of the few places in the country where people can walk into authentic rooms from an ancient Egyptian tomb and see walls covered with hieroglyphs that portray offerings to sustain the deceased person's spirit for eternity. The limestone blocks of these walls were purchased from the Egyptian government in 1908. They arrived at the Museum in 206 crates, weighing 96 tons.

Visitors enter the mastaba on the Museum's main level, climb to its rooftop, and then descend a spiral staircase to the mastaba's lower level. The gallery on the lower level features 23 mummies and explores practices and beliefs of ancient Egyptians in preparing their deceased.

Outside the mastaba is an ancient marketplace featuring artifacts from everyday life in ancient Egypt. Some of these artifacts were donated to the Museum by British archaeologist Sir W. M. Flinders Petrie. Appalled by looting in the 1880s, Sir Petrie became the first archaeologist in Egypt to record all artifacts from a site, even if they weren't gilded in gold. Unlike many early archaeologists, Sir Petrie also worked alongside his crew during excavations. In 1888, when the pyramid at Hawara was clogged with mud, he

BRONZE CAT
Egyptians considered cats, right, to be incarnations of the goddess Bastet.

FUNERARY BOAT OF SENWOSRET III
Originally on display at the World's Columbian Exposition, this cedar wood boat, far right, is one of six found buried near the tomb of Senwosret III.

stripped off his clothes, waded in waist-deep, and dug out artifacts with his toes.

The lower level gallery of *Inside Ancient Egypt* has a wooden funerary boat with a modern claim to fame. While scholars don't know whether the boat transported pharaoh Senwosret III into the afterlife or simply brought offerings to his tomb, they do know from tomb carvings that the king died in 1842 B.C.E. This information was used in the 1950s to prove the effectiveness of an exciting new scientific technique: radiocarbon dating. Radiocarbon dating is now one of the most widely used methods for getting absolute dates on organic materials from the past.

AFRICA

The continent of Africa is home to one billion people—nearly one seventh of the world's population, representing hundreds of distinct cultures. The *Africa* exhibition offers a small window into the varied environments, modern lifestyles, and historic contributions of this vast and diverse land. Some of the anthropological objects in these galleries are also considered significant works of art, such as the *nkondi* figure made by the Bakongo people, who live in Angola and the

LEOPARD STOOL
Possibly reserved for use by chiefs, this wood-and-bead stool came from Cameroon, Africa.

The Ancient Middle East

Inside Ancient Egypt builds upon a long tradition of Museum research into the early states of Egypt, the Near East, and the Eastern Mediterranean. In the 1930s, Henry Field excavated the ancient Mesopotamian city of Kish in what is now Iraq. Today, Museum archaeologists Dr. William Parkinson conducts surveys in Greece to examine how the Minoan and Mycenaean civilizations developed in the shadow of these earlier states. Meanwhile, Dr. Jim Philips works on archaeological sites in Turkey and Israel that relate to the same period. The artifacts above reflect the Museum's longtime work in these areas. At left is a carnelian bead necklace accented with chalcedony, amethyst, and lapis; at right, a stucco bust of King Shapur II.

NKONDI FIGURE
According to tradition, this artifact's use in settling hundreds of agreements among the Bakongo people endowed it with a profound, mystical power.

Democratic Republic of Congo. This piece is embedded with cultural significance. Traditionally, a wise man called an *nganga* invoked the spiritual authority of the nkondi to consecrate contracts and settle disputes. With each new agreement, the nganga pounded a nail or piece of metal into the wooden statue, which subsequently grew in its wisdom to judge right and wrong. Although such statues are often produced for commercial sale today, authentic nkondi that were used to arbitrate community life are rare. The nkondi on display came to the Museum in 1907 and is believed to have been used for nearly a century.

Other internationally revered pieces in this exhibition include bronze statues from the former kingdom of Edo, now part of Nigeria. These sculptures were often made at the direction of the *obas*, successive kings who ruled the kingdom until 1897. With their detail and craftsmanship, the statues are recognized as masterpieces of metal arts.

Toward the end of the exhibition, a simulated environment depicting the cargo hold of a slave ship demonstrates how millions of Africans were once brought to the Americas. Museum anthropologist Dr. Chapurukha Kusimba has been researching resistance to slavery in Kenya for more than a decade. The country's southeast, inland hinterland was once considered practically uninhabited. Since 2000, however, Dr. Kusimba has uncovered more than 250 archaeological sites indicating otherwise. He is particularly interested in three elaborate rock shelters that date to after the Portuguese conquered the coast, when slavery was

LEOPARD-CRESTED HEADDRESS
Beads and cowrie shells adorn this headpiece from Cameroon, Africa, right. The long blue beads were restricted to royalty.

IBIBO EKPO MASK
Power among the Ibibo of Nigeria was consolidated by a secret society called Ekpo. Masks like this one, far right, conferred anonymity.

institutionalized. Each shelter had exits that would allow people to sneak out, and elaborate fortifications that would have required cooperation to build. Dr. Kusimba's research reveals the resiliency and ingenuity of the Kenyan people, who formed communities and united in their resistance to the horrors of slavery.

THE PACIFIC HALLS

In 1909, Museum curator A. B. Lewis set out to "document as fully as possible the Melanesian peoples as they were before European influence." For four years, Lewis braved malaria, blackwater fever, and the swells of the South Pacific to visit nearly every island region in Melanesia. He returned with 14,000 artifacts, extensive field notes, and 2,000 photographic plates, making The Field Museum's collection of Melanesian artifacts among the world's finest. Soon after Lewis's trip, global politics and 20th-century technology brought such dramatic change to Melanesia that most of the ceremonial masks and sacred treasures he collected are rarely created today. The heritage of this rich

BAINING MASK
This mask, created by the Baining people of East New Britain, Papua New Guinea, is made of bamboo and bark cloth.

spiritual lore is preserved at the Museum, however, attracting visitors and scholars from around the world.

Three exhibitions are dedicated to the Pacific Islands: *Pacific Spirits* offers a glimpse of the time-honored customs observed by Lewis; *Traveling the Pacific* explores the natural forces that shaped the Pacific Islands and how contemporary cultures blend traditional and modern influences; and the Maori meetinghouse, *Ruatepupuke II*, is a symbol of the Museum's longstanding partnerships with Pacific Islanders to promote cultural understanding. Originally built in 1881, the meetinghouse is one of only three such buildings outside New Zealand. In 1992 and 1993, a group of Maori from Tokomaru Bay collaborated with Museum staff to restore this sacred space as a cultural outpost. The building and surrounding area are governed by Maori customs to create a *marae*, a place where people can gather as equals to explore differences and seek what unifies them.

EXTENDING WARM GREETINGS
The carved face at this roof's summit represents Maori ancestor Ruatepupuke II, whose arms reach out along the roofline to welcome people to the meetinghouse.

Skimming the Waves

For centuries, people have used canoes to island hop, navigating the waters by their knowledge of ocean currents and weather patterns. Before plywood and caulk became available, islanders often used driftwood logs as hulls and breadfruit sap as sealant. They also recycled materials to make the best of the scarce resources in their small island environments. The fisherman who originally owned this canoe found its outrigger washed up on the beach. In 1989, he and a master canoe builder traveled 5,500 miles from the Marshall Islands, bringing coconut fiber cord to assemble the canoe for display at the Museum.

THEN AND NOW: CULTURAL CHANGE IN THE PACIFIC

The early 20th-century villages that A. B. Lewis observed in the Pacific Islands may have had limited exposure to Western cultures, but they were far from isolated. Lewis's notebooks reveal a complex network that brought people from different islands into constant contact. For generations, these communities integrated new and traditional influences. Anthropologists today are intrigued by the habits of these communities, especially as many contemporary cultures worry about losing old customs amidst fast-paced globalization. To study lessons from the Pacific Islands, modern-day Museum anthropologists Dr. John Terrell and Robert Welsch followed in their predecessor's footsteps. They visited 80 villages in Papua New Guinea and 11 villages in Indonesian New Guinea to document how communities have changed—or stayed the same—over the last century. Along the way, they also uncov-

VANUATU MASKS
These ceremonial masks were made from cobwebs, coconut fiber, bamboo splints, and pitch, and adorned with boar tusks.

ered hidden significance in an ancient legend.

Scientists have long pondered the meaning of faces carved into South Pacific pottery more than 3,000 years ago. During their time in the Pacific Islands, Dr. Terrell and his colleagues observed a connection between these faces and the sea turtle images that decorate modern wooden bowls and platters. The persistence of this symbol suggests that socially and spiritually profound ideas are embedded in a creation story featuring a great sea turtle (the mother of all sea turtles). This legend may once have been as important to Pacific Islanders as the story of Adam and Eve is to the Judeo-Christian tradition—and its themes still resonate with islanders today.

The Regenstein Laboratory

In the Museum's early decades, technology had not yet developed to control temperature and humidity in artifact storage areas. Changes in atmospheric conditions caused objects to constantly shrink and expand, potentially shortening their lives. Today's storage conditions have improved dramatically, but even under ideal conditions, things aren't made to last forever.

Caring for the world's treasures is an awesome responsibility. So when paint peels, fibers fray, and wood threatens to crumble into dust, Museum conservators come to the rescue. Tucked in amongst the Pacific Halls, the 1,600-square-foot *Regenstein Laboratory* allows visitors to witness the conservators at work. In the lab, conservators consolidate flaking paint layers, stabilize chipping ceramics, and reattach fallen feathers. Each artifact is treated individually, based on the materials that compose it and the traditions of the culture from which it came. One team of conservators spent a collective 200 hours mending the gold and silk strands of a 100-year-old Japanese tapestry that would appear as the signature piece of an international exhibition (sometimes using thread no thicker than a human hair!). Another team used archival tissue and wheat starch paste to repair tears in a Chinese rubbing made

from an inscription at Mount Tai, a United Nations World Heritage site and the most holy of China's five sacred mountains. Such careful work enables the Museum to preserve cultural treasures—and the lessons they can teach us—hopefully for centuries to come.

LION SHADOW FIGURE
This piece is from Peking (now Beijing), China. Anthropologist Bertholt Laufer collected many such figures in the early 1900s.

CHINA AND TIBET

The galleries highlighting artifacts from China and Tibet are the legacy of anthropologist Bertholt Laufer. When Laufer joined the Museum in 1907, he was the only American scholar specializing in Chinese history who actually spoke Chinese. Unlike many scholars of his era, Laufer valued the cultures he studied as highly as his own. He set a new museum standard for presenting artifacts from the viewpoint of the cultures that created them—a key tenet in the design of contemporary museum exhibitions.

Laufer traveled alone and lived among the Chinese during his collecting expeditions. He once wrote to a colleague: "I came to love the land and people and . . . feel myself to be happier and healthier as a Chinese than as a European." By the time he died in 1934, Laufer had acquired nearly 24,000 artifacts for The Field Museum—spanning from 6000 B.C.E. to 1890 A.D.—made or used by the Han Chinese.

Laufer twice tried to visit Tibet, but each time was turned away at the border due to the region's political turmoil. Nonetheless, he acquired nearly 4,000 artifacts in neighboring regions, establishing one of the largest and best-documented Tibetan collections in the United States. The clothing, personal accessories, paintings, and sculptures featured in the *Tibet* gallery portray secular and religious life during the 17th through 19th centuries. When the exhibition opened, the Dalai Lama sent a personal letter from exile in India commending the Museum's "noble task, which contributes much towards the preservation of various cultures of the world."

Modern Museum anthropologists Dr. Gary Feinman and Dr. Linda Nicholas are continuing to investigate the roots of Chinese civilization. For more than 13 years, they have systematically walked the towns, farms, and forested hills of China's province of Shandong, where erosion, farming, and construction have brought ancient artifacts to the surface. They have found potsherds, ornaments, and stone tools that date back 2,000 to 7,000 years. This pioneering procedure has helped Dr. Feinman and

CHINESE AND TIBETAN MASKS
These masks, right, were collected during The Field Museum-sponsored Blackstone Expedition from 1908 to 1910.

MANDALA SAND PAINTING
Tibetan monks spent four days creating this mandala, far right, during an educational program in May 2007. Once the mandala was completed, the sand was swept up and released into Lake Michigan.

VISIONARY CURATOR
Bertholt Laufer (seated at far right) acquired the core of the Museum's Chinese collections. He is pictured in Hankow, China, now part of Wuhan, in 1904.

Dr. Nicholas to investigate the development of complex societies by creating a record of who lived where and when during the unification of China under its first emperor. This project represents one of the longest-running modern partnerships with Chinese scientists, who for many decades prior to the 1980s had been banned from collaborating with international scientists by the People's Republic of China.

ANIMAL HALLS

The seemingly endless forms of birds, mammals, reptiles, insects, and other creatures found in the Museum's animal halls give true meaning to the word *biodiversity*. The specimens in these halls are real animals representing real species living in real environments. Here, visitors can see such animals as a golden eagle feeding a hare to its young, an orangutan resting amidst the rainforest canopy, a rhinoceros and group of giraffes approaching a waterhole, and a nine-foot Alaskan black bear. On their own, the animals are striking, but the panoramic murals blended with

GRAND VISTAS
A hand-painted mural provides the
sense of limitless sky in this diorama
of marsh birds from the upper Nile River.

FOUR SEASONS DIORAMA (SUMMER)
Carl Akeley and his wife, Delia, made 17,000 wax leaves by hand for this realistic diorama, seen in the *Nature Walk* exhibition.

three-dimensional landscape details create the illusion of actually being with the animals in the wilderness.

Carl Akeley, known as the father of modern taxidermy, pioneered the techniques that imbue these scenes with life. During the 19th century, museums displayed animals in cases and stuffed their hides with straw and sawdust. Akeley, however, aspired to show animals as they truly are in nature. He took thousands of photographs while in the field and closely observed the animals' bodies and behavior.

Once he returned to his studio, he sculpted mannequins from clay, metal, wood, and plaster, and then stretched animal hides over the forms. Akeley was the first to present animals in natural groupings, with plant models and painted murals to complete the habitats. When his *Four Seasons* diorama of Michigan deer appeared at The Field Museum in 1902, it revolutionized museums worldwide. Museum taxidermists have sought to capture the essence of animals in their environments ever since.

STUDYING EXTINCT AND ENDANGERED SPECIMENS

Most of the specimens in the animal halls were collected a century ago, when many species—

and Imperial woodpecker, are now extinct.

Museum specimens are valuable tools for scientists who study rare species in the hopes of promoting their survival. A number of specimens in the Museum's collections, for example, provide a crucial look at African wildlife during a time when many of the continent's ecosystems were still relatively intact. These animals were collected during the 1928 Cudahy-Massee expedition, which traveled 12,000 miles through Kenya, Tanzania, Uganda, Rwanda, Congo, and Sudan. The naturalists on this expedition acquired 266 large mammal and 1,300 bird specimens. They also amassed 3,000 photographic plates, 40,000 feet of movie film, and cartons of field notes that documented the lives of the animals in the wild. While trophy hunters stalked the biggest males they could spy, these researchers collected female and young animals as well, preserving the animals' skeletons and skins. This rare set of data now serves as a benchmark in the study of ecosystems today.

particularly large mammals—were more abundant. Unfortunately, the first half of the 1900s was also the heyday of trophy hunting. People hadn't yet realized that the very size that made large mammals seem invincible, and thus worthy foes for the hunt, also made them extremely vulnerable as species. Consequently, many of the animals featured in these dioramas are now endangered due to overhunting and habitat loss. Others, such as the Mexican grizzly bear

The Man-Eating Lions of Tsavo

In 1898, the infamous man-eating lions of Tsavo temporarily halted the British Empire by eating a rumored 130 railway workers in what is now Kenya. Elemental analysis of bone and fur has lowered the estimated body count to 35 (but still plenty enough reason to not show up for work!). Scientists today suspect these cats attacked humans because dental injuries prevented them from delivering lethal bites to their usual prey. Research by Museum zoologist Dr. Bruce Patterson also reveals that lions in the Tsavo region look and behave differently than lions elsewhere. Tsavo male lions, for example, lack manes—as shown by the two on display here. Dr. Patterson is continuing to study lions in this region, developing strategies to reduce conflicts between Tsavo lions and people today.

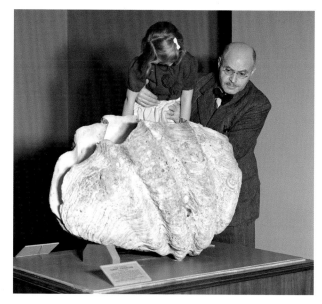

THEN AND NOW: INTRIGUING INVERTEBRATES

Despite the fact that invertebrates represent more than 95 percent of the known species on earth, it is usually birds and mammals that garner the most attention. As in nature itself, visitors to the Museum must look more closely at the dioramas to notice the dragonflies, crabs, snails, and spiders that make a habitat complete.

The Field Museum opened in 1894 with two curators to study birds and two curators, focused mostly on mammals and fishes, to cover the rest of the animal kingdom. Even as the zoology department grew, it wasn't until 1938 that a curator arrived to focus on invertebrates. Before coming to the Museum, Dr. Fritz Haas had spent 28 years studying mollusks at a German museum when the Nazi party pushed him out of his post because he was Jewish. He used the excuse of fieldwork to travel to Brazil; from there, he looked for a job that would relocate his family to the United States. When Dr. Haas arrived at the Museum to restart his career at the age of 52, his first task was to uncrate invertebrate specimens that had remained untouched since the World's Fair. For the next 30 years, he catalogued, collected, and conducted research to bring invertebrates their due.

Today, the Museum's invertebrate division has five staff members managing 4.5 million specimens—one of the top five collections in North America. Curator Dr. Rüdiger Bieler has gathered gastropods and bivalves from

PRUNUM CARNEUM AND *CTENOIDES MITIS*
A species of sea snail, right, and a bivalve, far right, were both photographed by curator of zoology Dr. Rüdiger Bieler.

PINNED SCARAB BEETLES
The worldwide scarab family encompasses over 27,800 species, one of which is the sacred scarab of the ancient Egyptians.

many parts of the world, including the Caribbean, Australia, and Chile, to study their evolutionary history by comparing physical characteristics and DNA. And curator Dr. Janet Voight is one of the few people in the world to have traveled more than 1.5 miles underwater in a submersible to study organisms living near volcanic vents on the ocean floor. These vents spew hot, acidic, metal-rich fluids in which bacteria thrive. Animals that can tolerate the fluids eat the bacteria, and can occur in amazingly high densities.

The more scientists learn about the world of invertebrates, the more this important group of animals has become integrated into the Museum's exhibition galleries, particularly *What Is an Animal?*, where lifelike glass models of invertebrates created by celebrated artist Rudolph Blaschka are on display. Insects merit their own zoology division, with 11 million specimens and eight scientists who study their adaptations and origins of diversity. Insects also have a hall devoted to them in the aptly named *Small Treasures Gallery*.

UNDERGROUND ADVENTURE

Underground Adventure is an immersive environment that illustrates the richness of the earth, revealing that far more species live below ground than above it. This exhibition magically "shrinks" visitors to be smaller than a penny so they can explore worm tunnels and discover how life underground intersects with life above. Each organism in this environment—

SUBMERSIBLE SCIENCE
Dr. Janet Voight uses this 16-ton, 23-foot-long submersible to gather samples of life from the ocean floor. The cabin inside this vehicle can maintain one atmosphere pressure, regardless of depth, and provide oxygen for three people during nine-hour dives.

EARTH EXPLORERS
Visitors get a bug's-eye view of the soil when they wander the worm tunnels of *Underground Adventure*.

Adventure challenges visitors to think differently about the precious world beneath their feet.

PLANTS OF THE WORLD

With more than 300 models representing every major plant group, *Plants of the World* celebrates the wonders of the green kingdom. Here, plant models portray creamy blossoms that ripen into cotton balls and eventually become jeans; a branch from a South American Cinchona tree, whose bark provides quinine to treat malaria; and the *Welwitschia mirabilis*, which can survive in Africa's Namib Desert for more than 2,000 years.

This exhibition was developed beginning in 1909 under the leadership of B. E. Dahlgren. A former dentist who adapted techniques for making false teeth, Dahlgren revolutionized museum plant displays in the same way that Carl Akeley changed the world of taxidermy. Dahlgren and his fellow Museum artisans meticulously molded, wired, and painted each model for the exhibit, starting with a series of plaster molds that were cast from actual leaf specimens and then

from the nematode to the crayfish—is 100 times its normal size. Yet every one is based on Museum specimens and designed with the accuracy of the most sophisticated models.

A soil lab at the end of the exhibition examines the relationships between people and soil, exploring the fragility of soil and how often it is taken for granted. The rich prairie soil in Illinois, for example, takes more than 12,000 years to make, but can be destroyed in an instant. By revealing this hidden world, *Underground*

MOLD-MAKING AT THE MUSEUM
Molded specimens like this *Welwitschia*—shown both complete and under construction—appear so lifelike that past visitors expressed concern over the expense of maintaining so many live plants.

Crown Family PlayLab

Children are just like scientists in their instincts for asking questions, observing closely, and experimenting. The *Crown Family PlayLab* opened in 2006 to create a microcosm of the entire museum that is especially designed to engage young children in exploring the natural and cultural world. Reflecting the latest research on early childhood learning, this 7,500-square-foot learning center contains six play areas for exploration and family fun. Children can carve fossils out of field jackets just like scientists do in the *Fossil Prep Lab*; plant, harvest, and grind corn in a pueblo like the one found in *The Ancient Americas*; or don animal costumes and step inside a diorama of the Illinois woodland similar to those found in the Museum's *Nature Walk* exhibition. In addition, children can make music on instruments from around the world, create works of art, and examine artifacts and elements of nature in a scientists' lab.

Welcome to the **Crown Family PlayLab**

Come in and explore plants, animals, people and cultures, and rocks and fossils.
What will you discover?
You can use your hands, eyes, ears, and even your nose!

filled with wax (and in later years, plastic). Other plant parts were sculpted using glass and more wax. Every model required multiple leaves and flowers of varying sizes to make it as realistic as possible.

The exploration of economic botany in *Plants of the World* is the legacy of Dr. Charles Millspaugh, the Museum's first botany curator. In the Museum's early years, Dr. Millspaugh acquired many resins, spices, medicinal plants, fibers, dyes, and cabinet woods to document the variety of ways in which people use plants. He also collected plants in the Yucatan, then one of the least botanically known areas of the continent. In December 1894, he embarked on a two-month expedition. Storms rocked his steam ship so much that laying out delicate specimens to dry was a gymnastic feat. When he traveled inland, he passed through such small towns that he was lucky to find a room to hang his hammock.

Nonetheless, through collecting and acquisitions, Dr. Millspaugh assembled what the University of Chicago's *Botanic Gazette* called "a great collection of valuable materials that should some day make Chicago a

foremost center of taxonomic research." Those words, published in 1924, were prophetic. Today, scientists throughout the world use the Museum's 2.6 million herbarium specimens to study biodiversity, medicinal plants, the effects of air pollution, and other topics.

Like Millspaugh, modern botanist and curator emeritus Dr. Michael Dillon specializes in tropical plants of the Americas—and in the flora of overlooked regions. Over the past 30 years, Dr. Dillon has conducted more than 40 expeditions to seek flowering plants, mostly in areas that were botanically unexplored. He has spent so much time in the mountains of Chile and Peru that he has been nicknamed "Dillon of the Andes." From his fieldwork, Dr. Dillon has created a website that includes more than 1,000 photographs and 2,000 pages of information on Andean plants. He also works with native citizens, universities, and other organizations to build local capacity for scientific research and conservation. The National University of San Augustin of Arequipa in Peru has recognized Dr. Dillon's contributions by naming a new scientific journal, *Dilloniana,* in his honor.

Meanwhile, other Museum botanists are leading the charge into different parts of the world. Dr. Matt von Konrat and Dr. John Engel have traveled to New Zealand (identified as one of 25 global biodiversity hotspots) to give the long disregarded liverwort its due, while Dr. Richard Ree has journeyed to the Hengduan Mountains of China, another biodiversity hotspot, to inventory plants and fungi. And so, the work goes on.

LOOKING OUTWARD
A view of the Chicago skyline is seen
from the Museum's north steps.

PART THREE

BEYOND MUSEUM WALLS

"Through science-based advocacy, natural history museums have become active participants in the struggle to investigate, preserve, and restore biologically and culturally important areas of the world."

—John W. McCarter, Jr., president and
CEO of The Field Museum (1996–present)

The Field Museum is recognized not only for the breadth and depth of its collections, research, and exhibitions, but also for its ability to make its resources accessible to others. Through fieldwork, technology, and artifact and specimen loans, Museum researchers share scientific data to help preserve the earth's natural and cultural diversity and to encourage sustainable living. The Museum also provides education initiatives and traveling exhibitions, making its reservoir of knowledge available to millions of people who may never set foot in Chicago.

Each day, the Museum works to impact the world—from local efforts to save migrating birds to international initiatives that lead to new nature sanctuaries in South America; from creating field guides that showcase a region's biodiversity to offering online access to the Museum's collections; from sharing scientific adventures with the general public to training future generations of scientists. Whether the Museum is gathering data related to a specific conservation question, promoting public education, or conducting basic research that may lead to untold future discoveries, these efforts make a difference. And while developments in technology and media from the past century have led to new opportunities for scientific research and education, the Museum's focus on understanding the world through natural history remains unchanged.

VAST COLLECTIONS . . .
A selection of zoology specimens, including lifelike casts of an alligator, a crocodile, and a turtle are shown at far left.

. . . SHARED WITH THE WORLD
Pictured at left is a tiny fraction of the Museum's insect collections.

CONSERVATION CLOSE TO HOME

Museum scientists have long been investigating a variety
of issues that relate to the environment in the Chicago
region. For example, research by collections manager
emeritus Dr. David Willard and ornithologist Dr. Doug
Stotz has inspired "Lights Out" programs in Chicago
and other cities to save migrating birds. Since 1978, Dr.
Willard has catalogued more than 35,000 birds (representing 140 species) that were collected at the base of
McCormick Place, the convention center just south of
the Museum. Over the years, he noticed that when this
huge building's lights were out after dark, fewer birds
turned up dead. Dr. Willard, Dr. Stotz, and other scientists had long suspected that migrating birds—which
typically navigate by the stars—were disoriented by
the lights, thus suffering deadly collisions. To test this
theory, the Museum scientists counted the dead birds
around McCormick Place each day during the 2000 and
2001 spring and fall migration seasons. They found that
when the windows were darkened at night, bird fatali-
ties were reduced by a whopping 83 percent.

A BIRD IN THE HAND
Dr. Doug Stotz holds a Golden-backed Mountain-
Tanager (*Buthraupis aureodorsalis*). This bird
lives only in a small range in the mountains of
Peru and is threatened by habitat loss.

INTENSIVE INVENTORY
Botanists collected more than 1,465 specimens and amassed more than 3,200 photographs to document a pristine wilderness in Peru.

In 2008, anthropologist Dr. Alaka Wali led research on a different topic: to identify how Chicago's diverse communities might engage in the Chicago Climate Action Plan, which aims to reduce greenhouse gas emissions citywide. Wali and other Museum scientists conducted ethnographic research—including open-ended interviews, social network surveys, focus groups, and participant observation of community events—in several neighborhoods around the city. They found significant interest in "going green." From this research, they also identified community gardens,

recycling initiatives, energy efficient buildings, and other assets that could help promote strategies for individuals and communities to reduce their carbon footprints.

CREATING NEW NATURE PRESERVES

Farther from home, The Field Museum works to conserve tropical rainforests. Rainforests cover less than five percent of the earth, yet are home to an estimated half of its species. To help protect them, the Museum's Environment, Culture, and Conservation division has created an international model that uses "rapid biological inventories."

Requests for these inventories come to the Museum from both national governments and local institutions. A year's worth of planning and

LOWLAND TAPIR
The largest herbivore in the Amazon, this tapir is one of 63 species of mammals catalogued in northeastern Peru.

collaboration then occurs before teams of botanists, herpetologists, ornithologists, mammalogists, and ichthyologists arrive for a busy few weeks of recording the species that make a habitat unique. These surveys provide solid scientific information to government leaders who are often deciding whether a region is worth protecting from industrial and commercial development. In the first 11 years after this program launched in 1999, these inventories led to 12 new protected areas, nine areas on the road to protection, and nine areas with their protection status strengthened. The total wilderness areas affected—mostly in South America—is equal to 95 percent of the acreage in the United States' National Park System.

In addition to conducting species inventories, Museum anthropologists help to identify opportunities for local residents to preserve their own region's rich natural heritage. In Ecuador, for example, the Cofan people are primarily responsible for managing a new national park created within their ancestral lands in the Andes foothills. Opportunities for other local communities have included agroforestry, ecotourism, and reforestation with native trees.

CONSERVATION IN THE TROPICS

The island of Madagascar is another place of particular interest to Museum scientists. With only eight percent of its original forest cover remaining, Madagascar is one of the world's most critically threatened

GONE FISHING
A Columbian/Peruvian fish team documented 337 fish species, including 7 species new to science, such as this *Batrochoglanis*, far right.

environments. It is also the most biodiverse of any landmass of similar size: In fact, scientists have long wondered why Madagascar has so many plant and animal species that are not found anywhere else. Museum field biologist Dr. Steve Goodman (an honoree of the John D. and Catherine T. MacArthur Foundation "genius" grant) lives in Madagascar for most of the year to collaborate with local biologists and conservation groups. He and his colleagues presented the first comprehensive explanation for Madagascar's biodiversity when they investigated the connection between areas of remarkable species variety and rivers in Madagascar that have headwaters at low elevations. Past climate changes had made Madagascar's lowlands drier than its highlands. As many animals retreated into the wetter mountains, those left near the lowland water sources evolved in isolation and diversified into new species. This research, published in *Science* in 2006, provided clear priorities for conservation at a time when the Malagasy government was increasing its scope of protected lands.

Museum scientists are also working to conserve the world's tropics by identifying their incredible biodiversity. To the untrained eye, these rainforests often look like a tangled mass of green. Because it's hard for people to care about plants and animals that

LIFE'S WORK
Dr. Steve Goodman examines mammal specimens at the Museum.

A Library of Life

Each year, the Museum welcomes hundreds of visiting scientists to its invaluable library of life, and sends approximately 40,000 loans of artifacts and specimens to other institutions. The botany department alone has provided more than 6,200 loans to some 1,100 institutions in 104 countries over 30 years. Collectively, these loans represent 750,000 individual sheets of pressed specimens that scientists elsewhere needed to further their work.

The Show on the Road

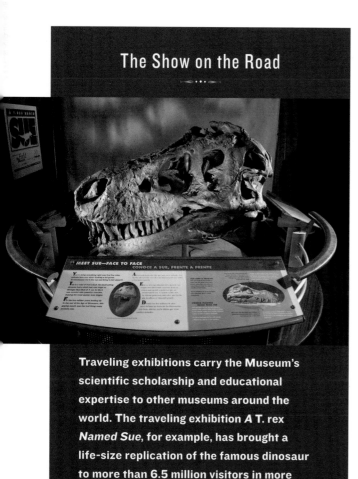

Traveling exhibitions carry the Museum's scientific scholarship and educational expertise to other museums around the world. The traveling exhibition *A T. rex Named Sue*, for example, has brought a life-size replication of the famous dinosaur to more than 6.5 million visitors in more than 51 cities, ranging from Boston and Atlanta to Bangkok, Dubai, Tokyo, and Singapore. In 2011, eight Museum creations were touring the globe.

GROUNDBREAKING GUIDE
Dr. Tom Schulenberg was the lead author on *Birds of Peru*.

they don't know about, Museum scientists are creating field guides. For instance, while Peru is home to 20 percent of the world's birds, no avian field guide existed until *Birds of Peru* was published in 2007. This landmark book—which features Museum scientist Dr. Tom Schulenburg as its lead author—contains colorful illustrations, descriptions, and range maps for almost all of Peru's 1,800 known birds. The book was created through a 30-year-collaboration among five scientists and 13 illustrators, who relied on Museum specimens for critical information.

To benefit species that can't wait for such a monumental project, Museum ecologist Dr. Robin Foster has created emergency field guides that can be accessed online. These guides offer colorful pictures to identify fishes in Bolivia, bats in Tanzania, frogs in Malaysia, trees in Panama, and other species in a total of 18 countries. The guides were downloaded 323,000 times in the first three years they were available. More complete data may be published in time, but these tools make the knowledge from Museum scientists available to others studying these habitats now.

REACHING OUT THROUGH TECHNOLOGY

The Museum also uses technology to bring scientific and educational resources to the world. Museum educators, for example, have developed many online

20,000 students, educators, and other individuals each year to follow scientists in the field. Since this website launched in 2002, followers have virtually dug dinosaurs in Antarctica, excavated a mountaintop city in Peru, and dived 1.25 miles to the sea floor in a submersible, among other adventures. Interactive maps, photographs, and email dispatches directly from scientists present an up-close look at science in action.

partnerships, drawing from the latest research on digital media learning to engage hundreds of thousands of young people. One initiative used video blogging, webcasting, social networking, and a virtual game called WhyReef to help youths in Chicago and Fiji collaborate on solving problems that are common in Fijian reefs. Students in both locations had direct contact with marine biologists to learn about reef biology and conservation.

Another website (www.fieldmuseum.org/expeditions) enables more than

Technology also increases access to Museum collections through initiatives like V-Plants, an on-line database of high-resolution images for 80,000 plant specimens from the Chicago region. This collaboration between the Museum, the Morton Arboretum, and the Chicago Botanic Garden was launched in 2002 and is one of the first partnerships in North America to allow users to search scientific information from multiple institutions

Training the World's Scientists

In addition to conducting research, Museum curators are working to train the next generation of scientists, increasing scientific understanding around the world. Many curators teach at local universities and advise graduate students and interns who come from colleges throughout the nation to use the Museum's extensive collections and state-of-the-art equipment. Each year, The Field Museum also hosts visiting scientists, some of whom stay several months to master new techniques. In just one year, for example, zoologist Dr. Kevin Feldheim trained 23 visitors—

some from as far away as South Africa, India, Germany, Italy, and Turkey—in methods of DNA analysis. Visitors come to study collections management, taxonomy, and a variety of other scientific methods as well.

Such investments of time and resources create ripple effects: After five students from the Universidad Amazonica de Pando in Bolivia trained at the Museum in 2003, they returned home to inspire 30 other students to enroll in their university's biology program, which hadn't attracted a new registrant in the prior two years. Museum zoologists supported this momentum by teaching short courses at the university. Museum scientists frequently teach workshops in the countries where they conduct fieldwork, and they train early-career scientists in the methods of fieldwork. This mentoring takes place in hotspots for biodiversity, geology, and archaeology, where strengthening local scientific capacity can have significant impact.

ENCOURAGING YOUNG SCIENTISTS
In additional to coaching scientific peers, Museum staff members educate people of all ages. Dr. Ryan Williams, above, demonstrates the attributes of Inca pottery for Chicago-area graduate students, while Dr. Michael Dillon, right, introduces young visitors to the joys of botany through the Museum's public programs.

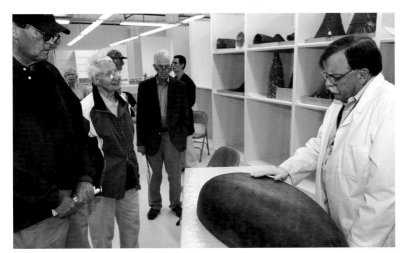

(with independently established databases) through a single portal.

The Encyclopedia of Life takes this concept further. As a cornerstone partner in this project—along with the Smithsonian Institution, Harvard University, and three other organizations—The Field Museum is striving to make information about all 1.8 million named species on earth available to anyone with access to the Internet.

Similar projects are increasing access to the Museum's anthropology collections. In 2006, the Museum launched a website with 20,000 object records and 5,000 field photos from ancient Kish.

Located in modern Iraq, Kish emerged around 3000 B.C.E. and is one of the world's oldest true cities. Museum scientists and peers from the Oxford University Museum excavated this site in the 1920s. Half of the artifacts found went to the Iraq Museum in Baghdad, and the rest were divided between the excavating institutions. (The Field Museum received two of the world's first wheels used for transport.) The website combines information from both The Field Museum's and Oxford's collections to make public as complete a record as possible from this important archaeological site. It is hoped that someday objects at the Iraq Museum will be added as well.

In the years to come—as technology continues to make new things possible, scientists continue to learn more about the world, and society's problems continue to shift—the Museum will continue to be at the forefront of translating collections, scholarship, and education into action.

ACCESS TO RARE TREASURES
A visitor examines a Kish arch in the Collections Resource Center during Members' Nights. A website devoted to the Kish collection makes information from these artifacts available to scholars around the globe.

PAST, PRESENT, AND FUTURE
A cast of the Museum's famous *Brachiosaurus* keeps watch over Chicago.

THE WORK CONTINUES

———◦ • • ◦———

A Message from
John W. McCarter, Jr.
President and CEO

Because they amass collections, museums are frequently viewed as storehouses of the past. While a good museum carefully preserves the past, a great museum continuously finds new ways to bring its resources to the public. The vitality of a great museum lies in its ability to increase and disseminate scientific knowledge based on its collections. For more than a century, The Field Museum has been doing just that—building scientific collections, conducting rigorous research, and exploring the interplay between traditional and new approaches to museum-based learning.

The Field Museum is committed to telling the fascinating story of evolution; to celebrating and conserving biological and cultural diversity; to bringing the world to Chicago through exhibitions, collections, and programs; and to using state-of-the-art information and analytical technologies to understand and communicate the complexities of the world.

At the Museum, we are grateful to Marshall Field, Edward Ayer, and the other civic leaders whose vision and resources created what is now one of the world's preeminent natural history museums. We are also thankful to the many generous supporters who make it possible for the Museum to continue its vital work today.

We know that you care about what we do, and we look forward to seeing you at the Museum again soon.

BECKON BOOKS

The Field

The *Field Museum* was developed by Beckon Books in cooperation with The Field Museum. Beckon develops and publishes custom books for leading cultural attractions, corporations, and non-profit organizations. Beckon Books is an imprint of FRP, Inc., 2451 Atrium Way, Nashville, TN 37214. FRP is a wholly owned subsidiary of Southwestern, Inc., Nashville, Tennessee.

Christopher G. Capen, *President, Beckon Books*
Monika Stout, *Design/Production*
Betsy Holt, *Editor*
www.beckonbooks.com • 877-311-0155

Photo Credits:
All photographs © 2011 The Field Museum except page *20a*, *GN8922oc* (© The Black Hills Institute, courtesy of The Field Museum), and pages *75b* and *75c* (© WhyReef and Numedeon, Inc.). • Kathleen Culbert Aguilar: *35a, A105154c_195790* • James Balodimas: *50–51, A111635c* • Karen Bean: *5c, Z94222c; 19b, GN91333_325d; 42a, GN91451_184d; 53c, GN91259_058d; 53d, GN91224_012d; 66c, GN91063_143d; 66d, GN91063_085d; 75a, GN90995_091d; 77b, GN91337_117d* • Rüdiger Bieler: *62b, MB1; 62c, MB3* • William Burlingham: *30a, wb4c; 54b, wb8c; 63a, wb11c* • Herbert P. Burtch: *13b, GN84635* • Álvaro del Campo, ECCo: *40, Ornithologists; 42b, Cordillera Azul; 71, 5_Plant_team_C3_2_ADC; 72a, 13_Sachavaca_3_ADC; 72b, 7_Ictiologos_1_ADC; 72c, 8_Batrocholanis_sp_ADC* • Charles Carpenter: *6, CSGN45101; 13c, CSGN44672; 14-15, CSGN63445; 15, CSGN40265; 18, CSZ6234; 31b, CSGEO3251 (hand-colored)* • Karen Carr (artist): *24a, GEO86500_052d* • Lawrence Heaney: *42c, cloud rat* • Wilfred H. Osgood: *12, CSZ56680* • David Quednau (designer): *26b, (3-D Theater Poster)* • David Rigg: *73a, GN90737_12c* • Elmer Riggs: *31a, csgeo3934* • Dov Scher: *24b, GEO86416_083d* • Cathryn C. Scott (contract): *76b, GN90457_6c* • J. W. Taylor/*Harper's Weekly*: *11, CSGEO6232* • Fleur Hales Testa: *48b, A109101_Bc* • Ron Testa: *back cover inset a, B83229c; 9a, A106659c; 9b, A108900c; 28–29, CK8T; 29, CK30T; 30b, GEO80821c; 34c, A110193c; 38b, A108352_1c; 38c, A108555c; 44b, GEO84880c; 45c, GEO84844c; 46a, A111518c; 47c, A109938c; 48c, a109452c; 49a, A106876c* • The Thompson-Starett Company: *13a, GN90799d_FMBL292wd* • Unknown: *5a, GN79223; 8, GN90799d_WFWC_21w (color plate by Charles S. Graham from The World's Fair in Water Colors); 10b, CSGN50750; 10c, GN86875; 16b, MH43_A; 23b, geo82014; 45b, csgeo62911; 53a, A112947_c; 55, A98299; 61, RF78998; 62a, Z81106; 65b, B83037c; 65c, B80027; 66b, 071210_Mandel-005571; 67, CSB4342c* • Janet Voight: *63b, EPR3* • Stephanie Ware: *17b, GN91139_55d; 69b, GN91139_29d* • John Weinstein: *front cover inset a, GN91368_01d; b, Z94466_13d; d, GN91262_021d; back cover inset b, A111269c; 4–5, GN90889_35d; 5b, Z94222c; 7a, GN88748_47c; 7b, GN89716_9c; 17a, GN91071_30d; 17c, GN91312_211d; 19a, GN91320_104d; 20b, GN88582_71c; 21, GN89805_42c; 22a, GN89758_12Ac; 22b, GN89471_78c; 23a, GN91262_144d; 23c, GN89035_9c; 23d, GN89036_36c; 24c, geo85894c; 25a, GN90846_158d;* *25b, GN90846_107d; 26a, GN90846_020d; 26c, GN91274_065Cd; 27, GN90846_173d; 31c, GN90600_035D; 32, GN90939_094d; 33a, A114463_02d; 33b, A114446_02d; 34a, GN90939_047d; 34b, A114465_02d; 35c, A114451_07d; 36–37, GN90960_495d; 38a, GN91013_41d; 39, GN90741_076d; 41a, GN90811_60d; 41b, GN91147_013Bd; 41c, GN91335_090d; 44a, GN91343_053d; 44c, A114389_01d; 51, A111277_25c; 52, A111270c; 53b, GN90689_18d; 54c, GN91020_190Ad; 56–57, Z94466_13d; 57, Z94461_05d; 58, Z93889c; 59a, GN90997_02d; 59b, Z94418_04d; 60–61, Z94352c; 66a, GN91064_013d; 68, GN90695_02d; 69a, GN91071_10d; 70a, Z94284_1c; 70b, GN91053_62d; 74a, GN90703_0203d; 74b, GN91053_85d; 76a, GN90717_66d; 77a, GN90764_012d* • John Weinstein (Taken from Gems and Gemstones: Timeless Natural Beauty of the Mineral World by Lance Grande and Allison Augustyn, University of Chicago Press, 2009): front cover inset c, GEO86518_0016Cd; 43a, GEO86518_0565Bd; 43b, GEO86518_4945Ad; 47b, A114680_011Ad* • The Werner Company: *10a, GN90799d_CG_004w (from Columbian Gallery: A Portfolio of Photographs of the World's Fair)* • Diane Alexander White: *16a, A112819_17c; 35b, A109925c (with Ron Testa); 46b, A109936c and 46c, A110745c (with Ron Testa); 47a, A112628c; 48a, A109327; 49b, A112518c (with Linda Dorman); 54a, A109237c (with David Rundell); 73b, GN90827d_1* • Mark Widhalm: *front cover (main), GN89776_12c; back cover inset c, GN90107c; 2–3, GN88769c; 22c, GN89667_8c; 45a, GN90408_09d; 64, GN89201_3c; 65a, GN89201_2c; 78, GN90107c*

Special thanks goes to the following people:
Primary review team: Jean Cattell, Lance Grande, Matt Matcuk, Nancy O'Shea, Laura Sadler, Alaka Wali, and Jeri Webb.
Topic review team: John Bates, Rüdiger Bieler, Beth Crownover, Gary Feinman, Kevin Feldheim, Steve Goodman, Jonathan Haas, Shannon Hackett, Philipp Heck, Jaap Hoogstraten, Anna Huntley, Dawn Martin, Robert Martin, Carter O'Brien, William Parkinson, Bruce Patterson, Olivier Rieppel, Leo Smith, John Terrell, Janet Voight, Emily Waldren, and Ryan Williams.
Photo archives: Karen Bean, Nina Cummings, Betsy Giles
Project manager: Amy E. Harmon

The Field Museum
1400 S. Lake Shore Drive • Chicago, IL 60605-2496
(312) 922-9410 • www.fieldmuseum.org

ISBN: 978-1-935442-11-0
Printed in Canada
10 9 8 7 6 5 4 3 2 1